PROMISE ME YOU WON'T LAUGH

PROMISE ME YOU WON'T LAUGH

A Cartoon Collection by

With an Introduction by Jill Jenkins

&

Foreword by Ken Mahood

Centenary Press

First published in 2000 by Centenary Press
7 the Meads
Cranham
Essex RM14 3YP

Distributed by Gazelle Book Services Limited
Falcon House, Queen Square
Lancaster, England LA1 1RN

British Library Cataloguing in Publication Data
A catalogue record for this book is available from the British Library

ISBN 0-9538699-0-3

Typeset by Amolibros, Watchet, Somerset
This book production has been managed by Amolibros
Printed and bound by T J International Ltd, Padstow, Cornwall

Acknowledgements

Sincerest thanks to Ken Mahood for his cover design and for his endless help and encouragement, without which this book would never have reached this stage.

Also to family and friends for their constant support and offers of help.

For Kim, David, Jo, Chris, Annie and Jane – and any other grand-children and great-grandchildren not yet conceived!

Contents

Foreword

'They spend their time mostly looking forward to the past.'
Look Back in Anger

And why not? The past, like a good wine, improves with age. I well remember in the fifties the excitement of buying *Punch* Magazine each week to enjoy the work of the exceptionally talented group of cartoonists who drew for it. A particular favourite of mine was Lawrie Siggs, whose contributions were invariably offbeat and witty.

Later, when I got to know him, I came to respect his skills and his pragmatic approach to life as a cartoonist. 'The only good cartoons are the ones with an editorial OK on them,' he would say.

A quiet, rather shy man, he was much loved by his friends and family and admired by his fellow artists. I now think of him as a kind of iceberg – a warm friendly one, that is, but what you saw was only the tip. Underneath that deceptive air of mild melancholia (a defence mechanism against rejection slips, I suspect), lay a vast fund of knowledge and an enquiring, humorous, idiosyncratic mind, capable of producing brilliant ideas on any subject from evolution to devolution.

The best ones, though, were about people and the minutiae of their lives, the details of which Lawrie absorbed like a sponge as material for his beautifully drawn comments on life. He could never really explain the process, but there was no need.

I think the secret of his success was his sense of wonder, which he never lost.

Lawrie Siggs is a happy part of my past. Luckily, his cartoons are part of the present – as fresh and as funny as on the day he drew them.

Kenneth Mahood

Introduction

Conduct - very fair. Wastes time sketching!

Such was the final observation on a very mediocre report, written in September 1918 about my father by the tutor, Mr Child, at the London Telegraph Training College. Amazingly, he subsequently managed to qualify as a wireless operator and circumnavigated the world five times before he eventually settled down to make use of his "wasted time".

Hence there is now a tin trunk in my mother's house that contains literally hundreds of originals – the life's work of my father that brought smiles to so many faces during his lifetime. They are just as appealing today as the day he tentatively submitted them to the editor of *Punch*, desperately hoping that one would be accepted to enable him to pay his bills!

Each cartoon has its own vivid memories for me, usually originating in family occasions and personalities. My father's love of animals and his ability to draw them is reflected in the fact that there are far more animal cartoons than are of any other subject.

One of my earliest memories was of a guessing game when he would draw a few lines and I had to guess what animal it was going to be. Often it would be a lion's claw, the tip of an elephant's trunk or three hairs in a pig's ear! He had a unique affinity with animals and children, resulting from constant praise, reward and encouragement – a method that I, too, have found invaluable throughout years of working in comprehensive schools.

My mother, an infants' school-teacher, prompted another large section of children-based ideas and a close observation of family and friends often resulted in their appearance in *Punch* the next week!

It is difficult for anyone who has not been close to a cartoonist to realise the intense concentration and hours of thought that go into the production of each idea. For each cartoon that appears in print, he has probably produced at least eight or ten roughs which have been turned down by the editor.

Much of my early life was influenced by tense anticipation when he returned from his Thursday trip to London; as soon as his key turned in the door, we knew whether any ideas had been accepted or not. Elation or extreme depression radiated throughout the house and lasted often until the next week. With no other source of income, there was always an underlying fear that he would never produce another acceptable idea.

Genuine modesty and probably a lack of self-confidence, meant that my father was both surprised and delighted when asked for one of his originals. A few were sold, but many more were given away, notably to the Queen Mother, the Victoria and Albert Museum and the Science Museum in London.

A particular request for one of his 'religious' cartoons came from a nun, who wrote to assure him that God would bless him if he sent it to her! He sent the cartoon with an accompanying letter saying that he hoped God would bless his gas bill, which arrived by the same post!

None of these cartoons would have been produced, had my mother not persuaded my father to give up his stable job in a gents' outfitters and risk everything with his artistic talents. As a young married couple with no savings and a baby on the way, this must have meant great sacrifices. Little wonder that life was a serious affair, though this could change within seconds when a funny situation appealed to him.

His laughter was infectious, made more so by the sudden contrast. The naturally serious, almost melancholy expression on his face was to serve him well in later years when, as President of the Hornchurch Rotary Club, he delivered his President's Night Speech. The room rocked with laughter – tears of mirth streamed down faces as he related a story of a Roman Soldier!!! I doubt whether anyone could remember the story now – it was just the way he told it!

This year, my father would have been 100 years old. Unlike my mother, who at ninety-four still lives a very full life, he dreaded the limitations of old age, particularly the thought that his working life might be curtailed.

A devoted family man, he would have delighted in his four grandchildren and two great-grandchildren. Sadly, only three grandchildren had the pleasure of knowing him, but hopefully this book will help the others – and any yet to come – to appreciate his humour, life and work.

OBITUARY, *PUNCH*, 12TH JULY 1972

"There's a car like ours."
(1954)

SIGGS

MANY have tried to analyse humour and many have foundered, and the good cartoon, that delicately-wrought craft object of humour, has suffered perhaps more than most from those earnest analysts. Scrutinise, attempt to explain, then the balance is tilted and the whole thing falls to pieces. Siggs's cartoons at their best are extremely finely balanced; their humour is the "delayed" kind—Siggs does not take us directly to the target but sends us through a series of ricochets until we reach the bull's-eye from an oblique angle. His cartoons have the knack (and the charm) of seeming at first sight to be not nearly as good as they are. Perhaps this explains why his work stands as high as it does in the estimation of his fellow cartoonists.

Lawrie Siggs died suddenly last week; the pencil roughs he had left in the office marked the end of a regular connection with Punch that had lasted over 35 years. A gentle, affable, *nice* man, he was invariably diffident about his work, but he could give wry overtones to an ordinary turn of phrase. As he once said, "A joke is only good if an editor picks it."

W.H.

"It's one of the best cookery books to blame I know."
(This was Siggs's last drawing for Punch.)

Couples

"That's the front door bell—will you answer it or shall I?"

"You're not even trying to visualise it on me."

"It would look better if we changed places."

"How about going out for dinner tonight?—
that smell has given me quite an appetite."

"You'd have thought that as I happened to have my instrument with me, they'd have asked me to play, wouldn't you?"

"Trust you to give me the sort of present you can row about whenever there's a tiny scratch."

"Really dear, that's hardly a woman's job."

"He wants his voting paper back."

"That'll be the new maid—keep this door shut."

MAUD'S BEAUTY PARLOUR

MAUD'S BEAUTY PARLOUR

BEAUTY PARLOUR

MAUD'S BEAUTY PARLOUR
SIGGS

"Do you mind?—we're just working up to a good quarrel."

"I get restless in the spring. I wish the council would make us move on."

"I can't see what you're grumbling about. It's all exactly what they showed in the holiday guide."

Sport

"See if you can chuck me into that blond's lap in the third row."

"I know that expression—he's hooked a nice fat order."

"I suppose any minute now those women will faint and have to be moved to the head of the queue."

"We came all the way down bumper-to-bumper."

"Don't you dare tell me I took my eye off the ball that time."

"They must be ours—we're the only two people playing."

"And may the best man appear to win."

"The tea urn's leaking."

"Would you ladies mind moving out of earshot, please?"

"What is a sign of when a cow is lying down with its four feet in the air?"

"If only I'd bought that model hat, now would be the time to tell him about it."

"The first thing you have to overcome, is the urge to laugh."

Women

"You throw me the money and I'll throw you a flag."

"You'll want your umbrella."

"Look, Mary, I must go; I started leaving my husband an hour ago."

"This will please Fred—he was afraid he'd be the first one to scratch it."

"Oh, is that you, Ethel? I was hoping it would be a wrong number, so that I needn't stop and talk."

"We've tried the horn, the trafficators and the lights, we know it's not them."

"...Then Timmy put his ball through the kitchen window, the potatoes boiled over, the baker didn't call, mary broke her doll, then that Mrs Jenkins poked her head in..."

"Of course the handbrake was on. Don't you remember, I'd just found out we'd been running with it on."

"I've lost a gold bracelet shaped like a snake with a special safety clasp, nearly new, value over five pounds, and a small child aged two."

"Why hello Ethel, I was just about to dial 999."

"Could you manage to put it right without finding anything else?"

"Promise me you won't laugh, madam."

"I already have one, thank you."

"Do you mind!"

"I'd intended going to the opera but the critics didn't speak too highly of it."

"It's going to put the whole thing in its normal perspective if we can say it was a mistake on your part."

WISHING WELL
SIGGS

WISHING WELL

"How about this one, sir, would you mind being seen dead in this?"

Giles

"Does anybody here own car number ZXY 303?"

"Do pay attention, Thompson—I said 'those ***against*** *my suggestion'!"*

"The trouble is, nothing's made to last these days."

"Hey, who's minding the shop?"

"I paint what I see, your Grace."

"In case you're feeling bloody-minded, I just heard what could have been a faint sigh of relief."

"But better the devil you know, surely."

"No, you're not interrupting a television programme."

"Did you ever! The swine has cancelled the meeting because of the weather."

"If you can't find the bell, try the knocker."

"I wonder if you'd mind being flavoured with just a tiny hint of garlic?"

"All my department wants is a straight answer—is this field ploughed or isn't it?"

"Kindly confine your questions to the working of this handle."

Health

"You mean she's actually out of hospital."

"Now that you're over the worst, dear..."

"Your stay in hospital has taught me one thing—I can undo a screw with a chisel."

"I get a sharp pain every time I do this, doctor."

"I got a few more manufacturers' samples this morning—let's try them."

"I'll think of it in a minute—the tune keeps running through my head."

"We've got it down to one of five things."

"Last time, failed to keep appointment, caused you considerable inconvenience, gave no excuse or apology."

"Ought we to send George one? He's donated his body to science."

"Oh, if you're running us home, there's no need for us to think about going yet."

"You might as well help yourself to a few roses, Alice—they're not at home."

"I keep telling her she mustn't pick them."

"I've found my glasses—you can all stop looking for them."

"We can't think why the Council doesn't order us to lop it."

"You ought to have seen the pile of filth I got out of the carpet next door."

"No, he doesn't talk."

"By the way, thanks for looking after the garden for us while we were on holiday."

"Not vertical? Rubbish, it's MORE than vertical."

"Ah, here comes the gentleman who usually helps us."

"Would three of you care to come and make up a four for cards?"

"No—this is the one I said was named Elsie."

"'Up the School' doesn't mean 'Up the School like Fatty Bucklestrap means it. It means 'Up the School' like Head Boy Brandon means it."

"He's being specially careful just to annoy us."

"Does retire immediately mean 'go to bed'?"

"If the worst comes to the worst, he can always go into his father's business, of course."

"Oh, for Pete's sake, let him dial it."

"Wave your flag, duckie."

"You'd have thought they'd have had the sense to make a door in it somewhere."

"When are you going to teach **me** *to shop?"*

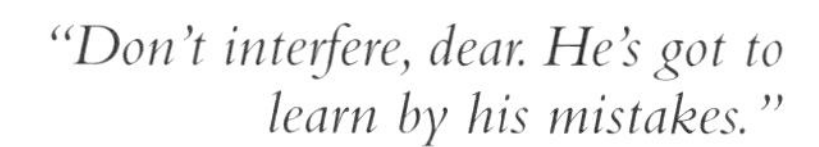

"Don't interfere, dear. He's got to learn by his mistakes."

"One of them needn't be dainty."

"Tell us to smile, Freddy."

"Isn't there anything we mustn't do?"

"I ***am*** *watching for the dicky-bird."*

"That you, dear?"

"Just once more round the bowl, George—then we'll have to ask the lady to make up her mind."

"He'll be glad to get it off. He hasn't bitten a soul for over a week."

"Very well then, hands up, all those who propose to become birds."

"How do you mean, life is what you make it?"

"I sometimes wish I'd left the damn thorn in his paw."

"He seems to be getting a pain about here."

"Now we'll compare it with his bark and you'll see what I mean."

"There's nothing wrong with you that regular food and a spot of evolution won't put right."

"I've been trying to teach him to bring my slippers, but he seems too stupid to grasp the idea."

"I leave the whole of my fortune to my faithful dog…"

"… And I leave my faithful dog to my faithful secretary."

"Well, funnily enough it did cross our minds that he might have escaped from somewhere."

ACE RIDING SCHOOL

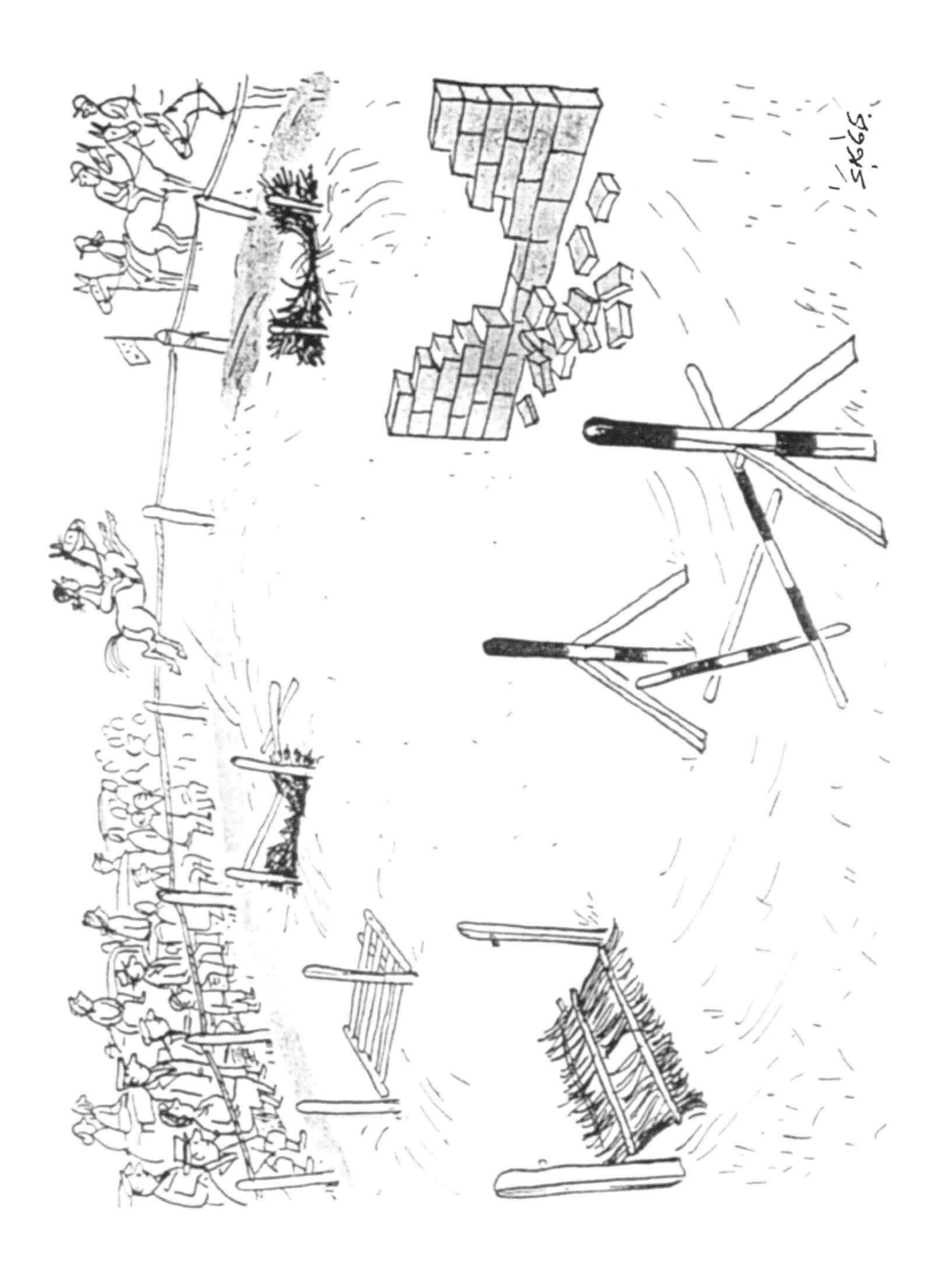

"He wasn't swimming anticlockwise before we asked Mrs Candleberry to look after him."

"We're hoping that one day he'll remember his errand and go off as mysteriously as he came."

"Yesterday, it got down by itself."

"Don't bother any more—I'll lay another one."

"Worst organised stampede I've ever attended."

"It all started when we had an argument about which was the most intelligent breed."

Religion

"Oh, I forgot to mention the secret passage."

"Mecca's this way."

"What bell? I didn't hear any bell."

"Tell us the first part of the one about the bishop and the chorus girl."

"Perhaps the Methodists prayed for rain."

"We must listen for variations—he's on the bells."

"Speaking from memory I'd say you've made her curves go in where they ought to come out—and her tail is a bit too long."

"Why, that would be the year Blue Peter won the Derby—in the old days, of course."

"Striving to excel at self-denial…beating the next man to the menial task…seeking out new physical discomforts…I tell you, it's a rat race."

"Just think, Doreen, only last night I was playing Bingo in Majorca."

"Do you think people have got nothing better to do than hang about all day while you find change?"

"That's the noise I mean, Joe—surely you heard it that time."

"It's a pity some of you people don't stop putting 'wish you were here' on your silly postcards."

"Know what I dread—driving home through all that traffic."

"One thing about not being invited, you don't have to make excuses to leave early."

"You get a good cross-section of opinion in here at weekends—half tight and half sober."

"They're English, I tell you—I could understand every word of their French."

"Wish I were there."

"Over in the corner, Marj—they're still on the weather."

Postscript note

The collection of originals will, I hope, remain intact and in the possession of my four children and then their descendants for the foreseeable future. Although the collection consists of some 400 originals, there are many more that I have been unable to trace. Should anybody be able to provide information as to their present whereabouts, I should be most grateful.